Joseph
and his Coat
of Many Colours

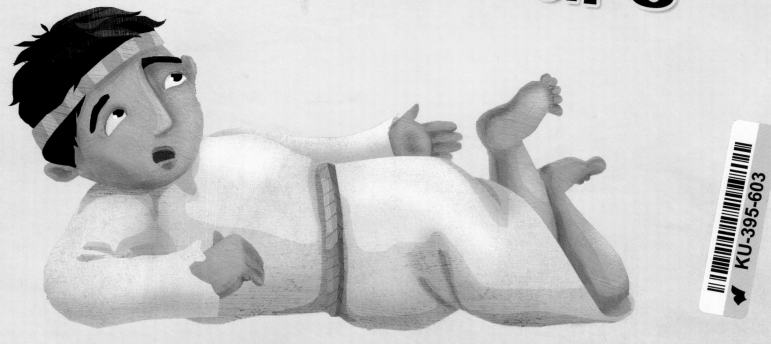

There once was a man called Jacob who had twelve sons.

His favourite sons were Joseph and Benjamin, but he **loved** Joseph the most.

When Joseph turned seventeen, Jacob gave him a beautiful COat of many different colours.

This made Joseph's brothers very jealous.

One night, Joseph had a strange **dream**. He told his brothers about it the next day.

"I dreamt that we were in the fields at harvest time and all of your bundles of wheat **bowed** down to mine."

Then Joseph dreamt
that the sun, moon and
eleven stars bowed to him.

When Joseph told his brothers
about the dream they became very angry.
"You think we will bow down to you?"

One day, Joseph went to look for his brothers while they were out **working**.

When the brothers saw Joseph approaching in his beautiful coat, they **plotted** against him.

"I wish we could get rid of him once and for all," one of the brothers said.

The brothers told Jacob that Joseph had been **killed** by a wild animal.

Joseph was bought by an Egyptian called Potiphar.

He was captain of the soldiers who guarded Pharaoh, the king of Egypt.

With God's help, Joseph did his duties well.

But one day, Potiphar's wife tricked Joseph, and he was thrown into prison.

God stayed with Joseph and helped him understand what the other prisoners' **dreams** meant.

One prisoner used to be Pharaoh's butler. He told Joseph he dreamt he squeezed grapes into Pharaoh's cup.

"In three days' time, Pharaoh is going to **pardon** you and give you your job back," Joseph explained.

Another prisoner told Joseph, "I dreamt I was carrying three baskets of bread, but birds were eating it."

Joseph's face fell, and he said sadly, "In three days' time, you will die."

The dreams came true.

One morning, Pharaoh awoke after two strange dreams.

In the first dream, seven fat COWS were eaten by seven thin cows!

In the second dream, seven small, shrivelled ears of corn swallowed up seven big, full ears of corn.

Pharaoh's butler remembered Joseph, so Pharaoh sent for him at once.

Pharaoh described his dreams to Joseph, and **God** told him what they meant.

"For the next seven years, Egypt will have good harvests," Joseph said. "But during the next seven years, the crops will fail and there won't be enough **food**."

Pharaoh was so pleased with Joseph that he put him in **charge** of Egypt.

For seven years, Joseph **stored** plenty of food.

Then the crops failed, and the bad harvests began.

People came from far and wide to ask for **food**.

One day, Joseph's brothers came, but they didn't recognize Joseph after all this time.

'I need to make sure they have **changed**,' Joseph thought to himself.

When the brothers were heading home, loaded with food, they were stopped by Joseph's guards.

The guards found Joseph's best silver cup in one of their sacks. Joseph had **hidden** it there as a trick.

The brothers were taken to Joseph, who said, "Benjamin must stay here. The rest of you are **free** to go."

"Our father has already lost his favourite son.
Let us stay instead of him," the brothers pleaded.

Then Joseph told his
brothers who he really was.
They were shocked when
they found out.

Joseph **forgave** his brothers and was reunited with his father, Jacob.

They lived together in Egypt for many years.